1

About this handbook

1.1   Introduction

This project was commissioned by the Department of Health as one of a series of exercises intended to investigate and offer general guidance with regards to different aspects of ethnicity and health. Related projects have covered mental health and counselling services for ethnic minorities.

The subject of disability and ethnicity has received only limited coverage. Recent reports like *Beyond Samosas and Reggae* from the King's Fund have been extremely valuable in raising the issues. However, there are few such reports (see *Bibliography*, Chapter 13, for full listing). This report was intended to build on the work undertaken by the King's Fund using the framework established in that report for a series of fieldwork exercises that could provide information on the key concepts; the main obstacles to service delivery; the types of self help and service provision that have been developed by or with black and ethnic minority people with a disability; and ideas, contacts and other help for those wishing to go further than reading reports.

1.2   The current context of service development

The initial stage of the review was to draw together and write to a list of what we hoped were lead officers in Health Authorities and Social Services Departments with responsibility for services for disabled people. (This proved something of a problem in itself insofar as it was not easy to identify which officers had lead responsibility in a given Authority and in some cases it was probably the case that no one did.)

Simultaneously we wrote to a wide range of disability organisations drawn from various directories.

In each instance the essence of what we were asking them was:

- what specific issues are you aware of with regard to black and ethnic minority people with a disability?

- what specific services are you providing?

- are there any self help or other groups for black and ethnic minority people in your area that are worth contacting?

The results of this letter, questionnaire and telephone exercise are given in more detail in Section B below.

What was particularly noticeable at an early stage was that those replying had little or no information to provide us with on self help or other specific groups. This may, therefore, have led to the conclusion that there are very few such groups. Indeed a review of much of what is written on this subject would also lead one to the conclusion that there is relatively little going on.

However, by following up those few contacts that were provided and others that members of the steering committee were aware of, over a period of some months we were able to make contact with and often visit a much wider range of groups than we had initially thought.

The conclusion that the review came to was that there is now very considerable activity, usually at a local level, where new and informal groups are being established. Very few have been in existence for any length of time or where they have, have often only recently received funding and been able to employ workers.

The groups that we met with were often unaware of each other and/or had limited contact with statutory services or the larger mainstream disability organisations.

1.3 Intended objectives

Given the current state of development of services by and for black and ethnic minority people with a disability it was decided that the most helpful approach would be if this handbook were to:

- summarise the key issues;

- describe the main approaches to the development of services;

- provide those interested with information on who was doing what; how to contact them for further information; and any helpful written material;

- by this approach encourage greater sharing of information and ideas.

1.4 Intended audience

The handbook should be of interest to all those in the fields of health and social care who are involved in the commissioning of services for people with a disability; primary health and social care staff working in the same field and particularly undertaking assessments; disability organisations; black disability

CONTENTS

organisations and other black community organisations and ideally should provide ideas and contacts for black and ethnic minority people with a disability
themselves.

1.5	Using the handbook

At each stage during the first half of the handbook – the 'Issues' section - we have
described a problem and suggested a possible response. We have then, whenever
possible, referred to further information that the reader might wish to look at.

Firstly, there are references to further reading. This is shown in the text by a reference such as **13.20** which indicates a particular report listed in the *Bibliography*.

Secondly, there are references to the field work studies. Where a particular project has attempted to tackle the issue under discussion there is a reference to the
relevant field study e.g. **Field Study–**.

The **Field Studies** are then to be found between the different sections and in the
chapter on the two area studies in Nottingham and Huddersfield.

Thirdly, there are references to projects which provided us with information but
which we were not able to visit. Details of such projects are included in the
Directory of Disability Services in Chapter 14 and reference is made in the text
to **Dir. 3** for instance.

1.6	The production of the handbook

The project was managed by a steering committee consisting of :

- Fitzroy Beckford   Black Disabled People's Association
- Donna Jackman-Wilson   Greater London Association of
  Disabled People
- Meena Jafaray   Artsline
- Meena Raj   CVS Consultants
- John Reading   CVS Consultants

The research and field work studies were undertaken by Meena Raj and John
Reading who have also written the handbook.

2

Definition of terms

2.1   Ethnicity

For the purposes of this research it was decided that the term ethnic minority would be limited to those people of African, Caribbean and Indian sub-continent origin only. This was partly because these minority communities are amongst the most numerous in England and Wales and partly so as to cover issues of 'colour'. This is not to dismiss the needs of people with disabilities from other minority communities.

The term Asian was then further defined to mean people of Indian, Pakistani, Bangladeshi and Sri Lankan descent.

In the report we refer to 'black and ethnic minority people with a disability' and sometimes the shorter 'black people with a disability' and mean by this the ethnic groups referred to above.

2.2   Disability

A report of this kind then needs further to state its approach to disability. The traditional approach has been based largely on those medical conditions that limit an individual's ability to carry out everyday functions. This understanding has been substantially broadened in recent years, largely through the efforts of people with disabilities themselves, so that the social model of disability sees disability as not simply a medical condition but as an interlocking network of factors which include the physical environment and social attitudes to disability as well as any medical condition.

Medical Model of Disability

The basic definition is then :

> *A disabled person is anyone who has a physical, sensory or learning impairment which prohibits their full involvement in a range of activities*

The Government's definition of disability is taken from the Disability Discrimination Act 1995 as follows:

> *A physical or mental impairment which has substantial and long term effect on the ability to carry out normal day to day activities.*

The World Health Organisation's classification of disability, which has been proposed in the International Classification of Impairments, Disabilities and Handicaps (ICIDH), identifies the following three different concepts:

Impairment – described as 'any loss or abnormality of psychological or anatomical structure or function'. This refers primarily to parts or processes in the body that no longer work.

Disability – defined as 'any restriction or lack (resulting from impairment) of ability to perform an activity in the manner or within the range considered normal for a human being'. This refers to the things that people are unable to do.

Handicap – defined as 'a disadvantage for a given individual, resulting in formal impairment or disability, that limits or prevents the fulfilment of a role (depending on age, sex and social and cultural factors) for that individual'.

The term '*disablement*' links all three concepts.

Social Model Of Disability

The Social Model then defines disability as the combined effects of impairment and social oppression. It shifts the focus away from the individual with an impairment towards society's disabling environments and its barriers of attitude. This model was developed by members of the international disability movement, and argues that it is society which disables a person with impairments thereby preventing their full participation in society. This definition provides disabled people with a group identity and a common cause.

A Social Model Definition of Disability

Disability may be described as the restriction in ability to participate in mainstream social activities due to the cultural, physical and social barriers placed by society which take little or no account of people who have impairments.

Field Study 1
The Asian People's Disability Alliance (APDA) Brent

History
APDA was established in 1989 following a conference called to address the poor take-up of services by Asian people with a disability. It now covers 14 London Boroughs and has over 500 members.

Services
Based in the Disability Alliance Centre in Central Middlesex Hospital, to date APDA has run three main services:

- a respite care project
- an information project and
- an advocacy project

though the last two are now only operating on a limited voluntary basis, as funding has expired.

The Respite Project runs two days a week and transport is provided to collect users. An average of 35 attend each day, some coming with their carers. All users have previously been assessed by their Social Services Department who then 'spot purchase' the day placement.

Activities provided include a range of stress management and confidence building sessions, office skills training, ESOL classes and life-skills training on healthy diets, etc. Alternative and complementary therapies are a key part of the service and they can provide acupressure, reflexology, homeopathy, aromatherapy and yoga.

The chair of APDA is a 'healer' and so contact healing is also available.

Issues
Many of their users were previously unaware of what was available and had had limited access to services. Users' perception of the health services available was that they were too restricted and did not include therapies like homeopathy.

Despite the intervention of APDA, users still have difficulties getting home care services. Partly the service provided is too limited and partly it is extremely rare to have an Asian home carer which would be preferred.

There are very few advocacy services, particularly for people who do not speak English.

Issues for younger people
Young Asian people with a disability are becoming increasingly aware of the new emphasis on independent living and yet there is considerable reluctance by parents to let children, particularly females, live independently.

3

Why focus on black and ethnic minority disability issues?

3.1   Introduction

The literature on the subject (see Chapter 13, *Bibliography*) provides a near unanimous perspective whereby black and ethnic minority people experience the same levels of disability and impairment as the rest of the population. Indeed some studies suggest general prevalence may be higher and some refer to specific conditions or illnesses which may more frequently occur amongst certain minority communities.

That literature then equally unanimously describes a situation where for black and ethnic minority communities:

- awareness of what services are available is much lower;

- take up of those services is lower still;

- there is a common view that services are unwelcoming or inappropriate.

There are a large number of reasons why this is so which this report intends to explore. There are pressing reasons why this situation must be changed and the report, therefore, describes various measures to achieve this.

In this chapter we firstly and briefly explore medical model type reasons. In following chapters we then go on to look at some of the social factors at greater length as it is our judgement that these are key to understanding why black and ethnic minority people with a disability receive such a poor service and what can be done about it.

3.2   Prevalence

The main source of overall information on the prevalence of disability in the UK is a survey undertaken by the Office of Population Censuses and Surveys in 1988 (see *Bibliography* 13.26).

After making adjustments for age (the ethnic minority population tends to have a much younger age profile) the report gives the following prevalence rates per thousand adults:

Table 1	
Prevalence of disability	
White	137
West Indian	151
Asian	126

The report comments that the differences are not statistically significant i.e. prevalence rates are likely to be roughly the same.

More recently the 1991 Census included more detailed questions on ethnicity than in previous population censuses and also asked questions about the incidence of 'limiting long-term illnesses'. There is clearly a question mark over whether a largely self-defined concept of a limiting long-term illness is precisely the same in all circumstances as a disability but there is equally clearly sufficient overlap with regard to disabling conditions for it to provide an important source of information.

The most detailed analysis we have seen is by the London Research Centre (data is for London only). Following similar adjustments to allow for the different age profiles of the different communities the report *London's Ethnic Communities* (13.41) drew the following conclusions:

- black children and children born in Ireland, had higher rates of long-term illness than any of the other ethnic groups;

- young Bangladeshi adults aged 30-34 had nearly twice the rates of long-term illness compared with white people of that age;

- Pakistani elderly people aged 60-65 had higher rates of long-term illness than any other ethnic group of that age.

From all this we draw the conclusion that disability is at least as prevalent in black and minority ethnic communities as in other sectors of the population and should, therefore, receive equivalent levels of service.

A related question is whether specific conditions are more prevalent. Clear examples are Sickle Cell Anaemia, Thalassaemia and Lupus which are known to have a higher prevalence in certain black communities than in white. Indeed incidence amongst the majority white community is virtually unknown. The key issue with these conditions is that primary health care staff are aware of the symptoms and that they are properly diagnosed. A number of the groups interviewed referred to widespread ignorance as to the nature or even existence of these conditions. (see Chapter 11 for a description).

More complex is the issue of congenital abnormality. Smaje in *Health, Race and Ethnicity* (13.40) cites a wide range of research to the effect that congenital abnormality is significantly higher for mothers born in Pakistan, India and East Africa. He then goes on to discuss whether this is a consequence of marriage between relatives (consanguinity), poverty or other factors.

These are complex issues well beyond the competence of this report. However, a common issue raised in the interviews was of those mainly Pakistani families where more than one child or other family member is disabled. Reference was made on more than one occasion to families where two or even three children are severely disabled. Whether this is more or less prevalent than white families is not a major concern of this report. What is of concern is that all such families should receive the substantial and varied support that they require. The Hamara Project described in Chapter 6 is a good example of a service responding to these needs (*Field Study 5*).

Field Study 2
The Organisation of Blind African-Caribbeans (OBAC)

History
OBAC was established in 1988 but services effectively commenced on any scale 18 months ago on a volunteer basis and paid staff were recruited 6 months ago. In their estimation large numbers of blind African-Caribbean people have not registered and, therefore, OBAC was established to make contact with them, encourage the take-up of services and provide advice on education, training and employment.

Services
They now provide
- advocacy work in Southwark primarily for elderly blind people;
- outreach work in Lambeth concentrating on the young;
- welfare rights advice;
- a talking newspaper on tape.

They are now planning to develop a resource centre with robotronic scanners – computers that scan text and reproduce it through speech synthesisers.

Issues
Only a very tiny number of black people have guide dogs and they are working with Guide Dogs for the Blind to help them promote the service to black people.

Issues for young people
They are regularly approached by 16 and 17-year-olds concerned about employment and training. Young black people who are blind wish to leave home and live independently but there is both parental reluctance to let this happen and an absence of appropriate accommodation.

4

Knowledge of rights and services

Introduction

There is a considerable body of research which confirms that a key problem for black and ethnic minority people with a disability is their often limited knowledge of the role of statutory authorities with regard to disability and of any services provided.

So, for instance, research by ADAPT in Bradford found that 'many Asian families have no knowledge of available services' (13.1). Other reports refer to the low take up of health information services by ethnic minority communities and that knowledge of a wide range of specialist health functions is extremely limited (13.13 and 13.23 for instance).

There are a considerable number of reasons why this may be so, namely:

- language barriers;

- health information literature not being received in the first place or being produced in an unhelpful format e.g. too many technical terms;

- isolation from informal and formal health awareness and disability networks;

- information not being available in Braille, on tape or in large print format;

- problems of communication with deaf people either through a lack of signers or through a lack of knowledge of British Sign Language.

To these must be added the widely held view (and a view supported by the Health Education Authority in their review of the effectiveness of health awareness programmes) that health awareness and service awareness is far more effective when carried out on a face-to-face basis.

Putting up a few leaflets in a Health Centre does not constitute an effective health awareness campaign and what is required is an active process of identifying, contacting and providing information to black and ethnic minority people with a disability so that, at the very least, they are aware of available services and entitlements.

4.2   A strategy to raise awareness of services

The strategy for improving awareness of services is then clear:

Table 2	
Improving awareness	
1	Involve black disabled people in the development and planning of an information strategy
2	Undertake outreach work to make face-to-face contact with black people with a disability using outreach workers ideally from the particular community concerned;
3	Provide information in a user-friendly format that is translated into relevant community languages and that is also available in other formats such as video and audio tape;
4	Outreach workers must lock into the informal networks that exist in all communities and use these as a channel of information and a means of making contact with otherwise isolated families and individuals;
5	Train and support service users to work with and provide information to their peers.

4.3   Good practice examples

Examples of good practice in this area include:

Table 3	
Good practice	
1	The African-Caribbean Disablement Association provides information and advice and generally attempts to raise awareness of disability issues within the African-Caribbean community in Walthamstow; (*Field Study 4*)
2	The Asian Deaf Women's Association in Newham do outreach visits to a wide range of community based groups to make contact with other deaf women and raise awareness of the issues; (*Field Study 3*)
3	Kirklees Social Services Department have produced a signed video on self help and services for black people with a disability, *Shaping Our Future*; (*Field Study 11*)
4	The Organisation of Blind African-Caribbean people employs an outreach worker to make contact with community networks and through them identify partially sighted and blind people who are not using services; (*Field Study 2*)
5	The Sickle Cell and Thalassaemia Project in Huddersfield have established a peer information and counselling service. (*Field Study 13*)

Field Study 3
The Asian Deaf Women's Association (ADWA)

History

The Asian Deaf Women's Association was established in 1991 by Sarla Meisuria, who is now its co-ordinator. As a deaf woman herself she was concerned that many Asian deaf women were extremely isolated. Few knew British Sign Language (BSL). Some had learnt Urdu or Hindi sign languages or communicated by gestures in a way that would only be understood by the immediate family. As far as she was aware there were no signer translators in London.

Services

From 1992 ADWA have been running a Tuesday women's group and over 50 women from all over London, but largely from the Newham area, attend. They also run a multicultural deaf club in Forest Gate which has 58 members and have run workshops on assertiveness.

A second part-time worker, Shafait Aslam, is now employed as an outreach worker and volunteer co-ordinator. They also provide counselling services for deaf women and their families.

They are very keen to increase the awareness and use of BSL amongst Asian deaf women and Sarla teaches Stage One BSL.

ADWA is a dynamic group which is keen to expand their services but receive only very limited funding for the work they undertake.

Issues

Some BSL terms are regarded as derogatory or racist. The sign for an Asian person is a thumb to the forehead and for an African-Caribbean person is a painted face. ADWA has proposed alternatives whereby Indian and African are portrayed by the shape of the country and a Muslim by praying hands.

Unmarried Asian deaf women may be perceived as an easy route to a British Passport by some Asian men living abroad and ADWA deals with a high profile of marital problems.

Issues for young people

Younger Asian deaf people are being taught BSL but their parents may not have learnt it and so communication remains difficult. There is, therefore, a real need to train Asian people to use sign language. One benefit would be that the children could be taught more about their own culture.

ADWA reports some abuse of deaf children including deaf children who cannot go to the mosque as they will be hit by clerics who do not understand the implications of being deaf. It was also suggested that some deaf children may be used for factory work. A key issue is a better understanding on behalf of some parents about the nature of deafness. ADWA refers to parents praying for deafness to be cured rather than seeking medical help.

5

Attitudes to disability within black communities

5.1   Introduction

There are three aspects to this:

- external attitudes of the white community as a whole and of white professionals to black and ethnic minority people with a disability;

- the views of black and ethnic minority people with a disability of the services on offer;

- the views of disabled and non-disabled people within ethnic minority communities.

5.2   The wider community and professional staff

External attitudes of the white community are profoundly affected by negative attitudes to 'race' and negative attitudes to disability. This is commonly referred to as 'double discrimination' or 'simultaneous oppression' or even 'multiple discrimination' if gender and sexuality are also taken into account.

It is crucially important to note that when black disabled people and black disabled women in particular, have been asked 'what factor has the most negative impact on your lifestyle' the regular answer has not been negative attitudes to disability or sexism but racism. (This is best described in *Reflections – Views of black disabled people on their lives and community care* 13.9.)

The field studies for this report looked more specifically at how issues to do with ethnicity and disability were dealt with by primary care staff and others involved in the field. The view we gained was of a widely varying situation from some very good practice to a great deal that was less satisfactory.

Dealing with the negative aspects first, common misperceptions include:

- 'we are open to everyone but ethnic minority users don't use our service';

- 'needs are dealt with by the extended family';

- 'there should be the same service for everyone and, therefore, measures to make contact with particular communities are not appropriate'.

There is clearly a major debate still to be resolved about targeting of services versus integrated services (see Chapter 8). Much more basic than this there seems still to be considerable resistance to undertaking active measures to achieve an integrated service in practice rather than just in principle.

5.3   A strategy for accessible services

The strategy for achieving services which are open to and used by all sections of the community can be summarised as follows:

Table 4	
Strategy for achieving services	
1	Using Census data and other means, have a clear analysis of the ethnic composition of the community any service is meant to serve;
2	Ensure that staff and volunteers are familiar with the key cultural and social issues for those communities (Karmi's *Ethnic Health Handbook* (13.21) provides an excellent introduction);
3	Make contact with groups and individual black disabled people to discuss their needs and their views of how these should be met;
4	Involve black disabled people in the management committee, planning group, consultative fora or any other mechanism for planning, managing and reviewing services;
5	Be prepared to accept that the current service may need to change if it is going to be one that black disabled people will want to use and that some of those changes may also be of benefit to existing users.

5.4   Views of black disabled people on services provided

There has been a limited amount of research to establish the views of black disabled people on service provision. We gained some further views by talking to users. There is then a much wider body of evidence concerning the perceptions of people from black and ethnic minority communities on health care generally.

Key issues raised were as follows:

Table 5	
Views of black disabled people	
1	An over-riding concern across both Asian and African-Caribbean communities was that people with a disability were not treated with respect. One project talked of African-Caribbean elderly and disabled people being treated 'like children by white professionals'. (*Fieldwork Study 10*)
2	Almost as common was a reference to a need for an awareness of religion or spirituality. There were two elements to this. Firstly that users saw religious observation as extremely important and that current care practices could conflict with these or simply not be aware of them. In research in Huddersfield with over 300 individuals 'following the teachings of your religion' was the top priority in factors affecting attitudes to health care. Secondly that services that only addressed physical needs were inherently limited and that what many users wanted was a holistic approach that included spirituality as a key dimension. (*Fieldwork Study 1*)
3	Other commonly expressed attitudes included: – services not having staff who could speak community languages including the different dialects of the West Indian islands; – services not providing appropriate food or drinks, skin and health care, entertainment or social activities.

5.6   Attitudes to disability within black communities

It is difficult to generalise about attitudes to disability within black communities and in some respects probably not that helpful. However, a number of comments were expressed to us most forcefully by some of the black people with a disability we met with as follows:

● Asian deaf and disabled women being regarded as a method of obtaining a passport by men living abroad;

● African–Caribbean people regarding asking for help as being beneath their dignity and that they would not want to survive on 'charity';

● a view that disability might be a punishment by God/Allah;

● a view that the family should be able to provide for the needs of family members and that to go outside was shameful.

The essence of most of these comments is that some black and ethnic minority people with disabilities and their families might not share the view of their white counterparts that a disabled person has a 'right' to certain services and should do their best to exercise such a right. Changing that attitude was a key theme in many of the projects we visited.

There were then some further revealing comments made about young black disabled people. Once again these represent particular observations rather than general assessments but still are of relevance for those planning or developing services as follows:

- a reluctance by some families to use overnight respite care particularly for female children;

- a view that some families were simply too protective;

- related to this a commonly expressed view by some of the young people themselves was that despite all the contemporary stress on independent living for people with a disability, there was huge resistance to this by parents particularly with regard to young Asian women and young blind African-Caribbean people;

- a concern that some disabled children may be receiving insufficient educational stimuli and, therefore, not reaching their full potential.

Field Study 4
The African-Caribbean Disablement Association (ACDA) – Walthamstow

History
ACDA was originally affiliated to the Waltham Forest Association for Disabled People but decided that it could be more effective if they separated and so was established as an independent organisation just over a year ago.

Services
ACDA is now staffed by a part-time Project Development Officer, Jennifer Ennis, whose role is to promote the group; organise activities, events and training; and provide practical advice.

The organisation is run by a management committee of nine African-Caribbean people with a disability and there are then a further 50 members using the services. The majority of users are female.

They undertake armchair aerobics; a range of arts and crafts activities including involvement in the local carnival and consultation with other organisations on disability issues.

The services are user led, with users planning the programme of activities.

Issues
It is virtually impossible to get African-Caribbean food in hospital and so the group visits members who are hospitalised and brings food.

Hospital services, according to ACDA, have very little awareness of the conditions of Sickle Cell Anaemia and Lupus.

6

Low levels of service take up

6.1   Introduction

Many of the projects that we visited have come into existence because of a concern about the low level of take up of services by people from black and ethnic minority communities.

In Kirklees (*Field Study 11*) workers were employed through Home Office Section 11 funding to undertake outreach with ethnic communities and the result was that use of disability services across the board increased from 2 to 15 per cent.

There is clearly no excuse for disability services which are situated in or service significant concentrations of ethnic minority communities, to have low or no take up from these communities.

Various reports have been published recently, all commissioned by the Department of Health; amongst them *Checklist on Health and Race* and *Facing up to Difference* (Refs 13.17 and 13.11) which are intended to encourage and assist health and social care managers to provide effective services to their ethnic communities.

6.2   Improving take up of services

There are a number of clear practical steps that can be taken to encourage the use of services.

Table 6:	
Improving service take up	
1	Employ Asian and African-Caribbean staff within disability services and/or as outreach workers to their communities;
2	Where Asian and African-Caribbean specialist staff are not available or cannot be recruited in the short term, consider approaches like co-working (*Field Study 9*);
3	Encourage self-help and other black and ethnic minority disability groups to use mainstream disability premises for their meetings;
4	Make links with Dial-a-Ride and community transport schemes for ethnic minorities to help with access arrangements;

contd

5	Review reception arrangements to ensure they are welcoming and informative;
6	Ensure that staff are available who speak community languages and signers or have access to interpreters;
7	If meals or snacks are provided ensure they are appropriate.

6.3 Good practice examples

Examples of good practice in this area include the following:

Table 7

Good practice

1	The Disabilities Living Centre in Nottingham employs an Asian Development Worker to promote the service to community groups in the area and undertake training for professional staff; (*Field Study 11*)
2	Nottingham Community Health NHS Trust is running a two year pilot stroke project using an African-Caribbean and an Asian co-worker to operate as intermediaries between families and professional staff; (*Field Study 9*)
3	Kirklees Social Services Department employs a black social worker with a disability to undertake assessments of black disabled people and to advise colleagues on related issues. (*Field Study 12*)

Field Study 5

The Hamara Project

History

The Hamara Project was established by Barnardo's, the national children's charity, to provide services to ethnic minority children with a disability in Waltham Forest.

Waltham Forest Social Services Department had undertaken considerable joint work with Asian communities previously so there was a substantial body of experience to build on.

contd

Services

The Hamara Team consisting of a Co-ordinator, a Hindu social worker and a Muslim social worker, provide three main services:

- a respite care service;
- a sitting service;
- a befriending service.

The respite care entails placing a child with foster parents to give the parents a break. They have a same-race policy for family placements.

With the sitting service a volunteer will come into the family's own home to enable parents to go out shopping etc. Finally they are developing a befriending service for older children which involves taking the children out and participating in social and educational activities. They are dealing with approximately 70 children of whom 28 receive respite care and 38 the sitting service.

An Asian Parents and Carers group is now well established and consists of some forty to fifty families. A Black Support Group is at an earlier stage of development but still attracts twenty families. Hamara then provides carers training on disability awareness, child protection and separation from parents.

Issues

It is reasonably common, particularly amongst the Pakistani Muslim families, for there to be more than one child in a family with a disability implying that the cause is genetic and requiring considerable support resources.

There is difficulty recruiting African-Caribbean carers, partly because many black women are working. Asian carers, after an initial reluctance to come forward and an anxiety about making mistakes, are then very keen to receive training.

Issues for young people

Families are reluctant to use overnight respite care particularly for Asian adolescent girls. Asian families tend to be very protective and want to provide all the care themselves.

There is a concern that some of the children are receiving insufficient educational stimulus including play and so Hamara is developing a toy library.

7

The appropriateness of the service provided

7.1   Introduction

Providing information on health awareness and availability of services, and reviewing organisational and staffing arrangements are only part of the total equation.

The other key element is to consider whether appropriate services are being provided. Only black and ethnic minority people with a disability can ultimately decide what is appropriate for them. User choice must be the first principle. However, given the management of health and social resources, consultation with users over the best use of limited resources must be the second.

7.2   Key choices

Based on the field work studies we became aware of a number of key choices that users may wish to exercise:

Table 8	
Key choices	
1	Many Asian people with a disability consciously choose to meet together rather than in an integrated group. This seems to be less the case for younger Asian people. For the African-Caribbean community there were also many similar examples but also cases across the age range where people were happy to participate in mixed race groups;
2	Some Asian women and some African-Caribbean women prefer women only groups;
3	Wherever possible there is a preference for services to be locally based and in a secure environment;
4	Many users would prefer to have home care workers from the same ethnic background;
5	Women users would nearly always prefer to have female home care workers.

SECTION A: ISSUES

7.3   Good practice examples

Examples of good practice in this area include the following:

Table 9
Good practice

1	The Waltham Forest Disability Centre runs separate groups for Asian men and for Asian women; (*Field Study 7*)
2	In Huddersfield the African-Caribbean Women's Disability Project holds regular women only meetings; (*Field Study 14*)
3	The stroke group in Nottingham meets in the local Indian Community Centre; (*Field Study 8*)
4	The Community Care Service for the African-Caribbean Community in Leyton uses African-Caribbean home care workers to provide services to disabled, frail and elderly people in their own homes; (*Dir. 8*)
5	Kirklees Social Services is attempting to recruit Asian female homecarers as this is a clearly expressed preference of users. (*Field Study 12*)

7.4   Difference in services provided

Other than ethnicity and gender issues regarding who provides and who uses different services, the nature of what was actually provided tended to vary from what was provided for white users more in terms of making it culturally appropriate than the actual substance of what was on offer. Examples include the following:

Table 10
Making services culturally appropriate

1	Reworking British Sign Language to remove gestures that were regarded as racist or derogatory;
2	Using prayer as a key activity for a stroke group;
3	Using Asian or African-Caribbean music for movement activities;
4	Users learning or undertaking craft activities that derived from their own culture (though there was also considerable interest from women in particular for Asian women to learn craft and cookery skills from African-Caribbean women and vice versa).

7.5	Alternative and complementary therapies

The main area in which new services were being developed was in alternative or complementary therapies and traditional healing techniques. Whilst these are starting to be explored in some mainstream services they are regularly an integral and automatic part of ethnic minority services.

Table 11	
Using different therapies	
1	The use of yoga for stroke victims (*Field Study 8*)
2	A hakim or traditional faith healer being available (*Field Study 1*)
3	The regular use of acupressure, reflexology and aromatherapy (*Field Study 1*)
4	Homoeopathic and Ayurvedic systems of medicine (*Field Study 1*)
5	Meditation to 'help the balance of mind, body and soul' (*Field Study 8*)

Field Study 6

Brent African-Caribbean Disabled People's Association (BACDPA)

History

BACDPA was originally established as the Brent Black People's Disablement Association and only recently changed its name. The service was started three years ago but has only had a paid worker for the past few months.

Services

BACDPA is based in the same Disability Alliance Centre as APDA (see *Field Study 1* above) and, therefore, share the training facilities and meeting rooms. They now have 150 members, not all of whom are active, and run:

- the You and I Sickle Cell Anaemia group;
- workshops and courses in basic English, computers and design;
- Music and Art Therapy Groups;
- Advocacy and general support groups;
- Welfare Benefits and primary care services promotion sessions.

A key project is to encourage younger disabled people to work with and train older disabled members. The committee includes three younger black disabled members and this is regarded as good training in its own right.

BACDPA aims to work towards the reduction of unemployment amongst African-Caribbean disabled people, and to raise awareness of the particular issues they face.

BACDPA also works in conjunction with other disability organisations to develop appropriate services for disabled people.

Issues

Recruiting volunteers is proving very difficult and BACDPA wants to devote considerable energy to promoting self help in the community.

8

Integration versus targeting

8.1	Prevalence

Undertaking a review to establish whether Authorities and other agencies were providing specific services for black and ethnic minority people with a disability, we found there was very considerable resistance to, or disagreement with the concept that different communities either required different services or even required additional efforts to encourage them to take up existing services.

It is important to make clear that this was far from being a majority position. However, this view was represented so forcefully by some respondents that we felt the issues had to be explored further.

At a basic level this was represented by what has been described as the 'colour blind' approach e.g.:

> *We do not keep statistics on the ethnic origins of our clients as we deem this is not in line with our equal opportunities policy. All clients are treated as equals without any bias or discrimination.*

The issue for all providers must be that not only should they have an equal opportunities policy but also that they should have measures in place to establish whether it is working and corrective action in mind if it is not. Ethnic monitoring is a basic tool for monitoring the effectiveness of equal opportunities.

The experience of this review is that the vast majority of providers either had ethnic monitoring systems in place or were in the process of implementing them. Health Authorities in particular referred to the requirement for in-patient monitoring of ethnicity from April 1995 and their intention simultaneously to apply this to community based services. A local and national analysis of this data in due course will be very important.

A more thoughtful approach to the underlying issue of integration versus separate services was put as follows:

> *It could be argued from some points of view that integration is a fundamental philosophy which ought to be being adopted so that there should not be separate facilities for disabled people and that there should not be special facilities for ethnic minority clients.*

The overwhelming view to arise from the consultation we undertook with purchasers, providers and black and ethnic minority disabled people is that it is not a question of either integrated services or separate services but both.

8.2	The integration of services

With regard to the integration of services the overall view can be summarised as follows:

Table 11	
Integrating services	
1	All people with a disability, regardless of ethnicity, should be able to have reasonable access to public places and facilities and participate in day to day activities;
2	There is an expectation by the Department of Health and a demand by black people with a disability that all Health and Social Care Authorities should ensure their services are accessible and appropriate;
3	All public services should monitor not just ethnicity and disability but gender and sexuality to ensure that they genuinely serve the entire community in which they are situated;
4	All such public services should take positive measures to improve take up where it becomes evident through monitoring that a particular group is not using those services.

This, however, only represents stage one of the debate. There are many examples, often from other health or social care sectors, of provider agencies working very industriously to implement the four steps described above and yet not succeeding.

Good intentions will not necessarily overcome barriers created by historic discrimination, by mistrust or lack of information and by the very simple fact that what is on offer is not what is wanted.

One example is from the field of counselling where many of the larger counselling agencies had endeavoured for some years to tackle the issue that service users were predominantly white even where services where located near or in Asian or African-Caribbean communities. Those efforts had largely failed. The turning point was the development of services specifically targeted to either Asian or African-Caribbean users employing counsellors from those communities. Those targeted services then experienced a major success in attracting and helping ethnic minority clients who needed counselling.

That process was subject to considerable resistance in the first place and from some sectors still probably is. However, within the counselling field a number of key understandings have emerged as to how to provide effective counselling for black and ethnic minority clients as follows:

- counselling is far more effective when it is in the client's mother tongue;

- clients preferred to be counselled by someone with a similar ethnic background;

- counselling as a concept is very much Western in origin and needs careful explanation to people who are not familiar with it;

- the most commonly used models of counselling needed rethinking to place greater emphasis on the family dimension, on culture and on religion.

That experience has helped the mainstream services to rethink how they go about making their services more widely accessible.

8.3   The development of separate services

With regard to the development of separate services the argument can be summarised as follows:

Table 12
Developing separate services
1   Black and ethnic minority people with a disability regularly choose services shared with people from a similar background for a whole variety of reasons to do with shared experiences;
2   At the present stage of service development virtually the only means of accessing services where the right language, diet and awareness of other religious and cultural expectations are provided, is through separate services;
3   Some of the separate services being developed differ significantly from mainstream services not just on grounds of language and culture but in terms of what is being offered. At present that difference is largely to do with complementary therapies and the dimension of faith or spirituality. Other factors may emerge.
4   A key dynamic in the whole disability movement is empowerment through self help or taking charge of one's own destiny. This is precisely what many of these separate services are attempting to do.

It is important to note that the review found that much of the activity described in the field studies was at a very early stage of development – groups had only very recently been set up or workers appointed. Much more detailed information on models of self help and service provision will, therefore, emerge as this work consolidates and develops and new groups are formed.

However, the early experience suggests a similar pattern to other sectors, such as counselling, whereby a large number of black and ethnic minority people will use separate services who would not, at this stage, use integrated services; and that in due course they and others like them may be more prepared to use integrated services if those services can be seen to have genuinely learnt and adapted themselves to the lessons arising from the efforts of black groups.

Field Study 7
Waltham Forest Disability Centre

History
The Disability Centre is a voluntary organisation which has a service level agreement with Waltham Forest Social Services Department to provide a wide range of activities (approximately 20) for people with a disability within the Centre.

Based in a part of London which has a substantial African-Caribbean and Asian population they had been conscious for some time of the poor level of take up from these communities. Following a substantial programme of outreach work to community groups by the Centre Manager, Mrs Khan, the number of Asian users has increased significantly and specific services are now provided. The number of African-Caribbean users also increased but to a lesser extent. An African-Caribbean users' group was started but did not succeed and has now been integrated with other activities.

Services
The Centre now has 220 regular users of whom 67 are Asian and 31 are African-Caribbean.

Experience has shown that some Asian and African-Caribbean users are happy to participate in services with other white users whereas others prefer a separate group. A youth group, for instance, meets on Wednesday evenings comprising Asian and white young people. Asian women users, on the other hand, wanted a separate group which now meets weekly for keep fit, cookery classes and outings. There is also an Asian men's group.

A deaf outreach worker is contacting schools presently and a disabled volunteer is contacting agencies to encourage continued take up of services.

contd

Issues

A number of Asian and African-Caribbean users have not registered with Social Services and are unaware of the services to which they are entitled. The view of a group of users at the Centre was that registration was a complete waste of time. There is only a very limited concept of taking up services and a reluctance to receive 'charity'.

Severely disabled users need live-in carers but it is difficult to find these from the same ethnic community.

The local college is not wheelchair accessible and so the Centre is negotiating to run some courses directly.

9

Meeting needs

9.1   Introduction

This section of the report looks at different approaches to meeting needs.

The first section considers various approaches to enabling improved access to services. The second considers a number of key themes in the services that are then provided that have not been covered so far.

9.2   Improving access: enabling through communication

It is difficult to articulate your own needs and demands if you do not share a language with the person who controls the resources or has the skills you are looking for. Language and communication can have a wide range of aspects or implications in this context as follows:

Table 13	
Some points about language	
1	There are very few advocates who speak languages other than English;
2	For many first generation people from ethnic minorities fluency in English may be limited or non-existent;
3	Many deaf people from ethnic minorities do not know British Sign Language (BSL). Where they do, their parents or carers may not know it. Ethnic minority deaf people are likely to feel uncomfortable or offended by some aspects of BSL. After all, the BSL sign for an African-Caribbean person is a painted face and for an Asian person a thumb to the forehead;
4	Elderly African-Caribbean people may be assumed to want to communicate in standard English whereas their actual language may be one of the very many different dialects spoken in the West Indies;
5	Blind people may need audio tapes to be translated.

Responses to these issues that we came across in the field work studies include the following:

Table 14	
Some responses	
1	Information packs and audio tapes in different languages; (*Field Study 12*)
2	The use of Asian and African-Caribbean co-workers to act as intermediaries between families and professionals; (*Field Study 9*)
3	Training for deaf people and their carers in BSL and attempts to change derogatory gestures so that the sign for an Asian person is the shape of India and for an African person the shape of Africa. (*Field Study 3*)

9.3   Improving access: enabling through mobility

One of the most common problems described to us was of the isolation experienced by some disabled people. Even when living in a family setting it may be virtually impossible to get out and meet friends socially or go shopping for instance. Specific examples were as given below:

Table 15	
Some examples	
1	Only a very tiny number of Asian and African-Caribbean blind people have a guide dog;
2	Electronic wheelchairs and other more sophisticated means of mobility may be prohibitively expensive for poorer people;
3	Many areas are not served by Dial a Ride or transport provided by Social Services;

Responses to these issues that we came across in the field work studies include the following:

Table 16	
Some responses	
1	A joint project between an organisation for black blind people and the national Guide Dogs for the Blind organisation to provide more guide dogs for black people; (*Field Study 2*)
2	A project to encourage Asian and African-Caribbean disabled people to use a disability resources centre; (*Field Study 7*)
3	A number of cases where volunteers and family members were providing transport, for instance. (*Field Study 8*)

9.4   Improving access: enabling through facilities

Where black and ethnic minority people with a disability do wish to develop self-help groups or participate in organised groups there is often a basic problem as to where these activities can take place. If, as already described there is an unwillingness to use what are perceived to be white centres and if there are no local facilities then there will be clear problems in getting activities off the ground. Specific responses to this were as shown below:

Table 17	
Some responses	
1	A stroke group using a room in the local Indian Community Centre; (*Field Study 8*)
2	A disused primary school being converted for use as a disability centre; (*Field Study 7*)
3	And best of all specially designed new premises for use by African-Caribbean and Asian disability groups; (*Field Studies 1 and 6*)

9.5   Developing services: respite services

The need for respite services is likely to be no different for Asian and African-Caribbean people than for others. However, there are a number of specific factors that make the provision of respite care that much more difficult as follows:

Table 18	
Specific factors	
1	Carers' support structures in some areas are largely white and there, is, therefore, a need to develop black carers' groups, etc.;
2	Respite care in the home is often unwelcome unless it is someone from the same culture; gender issues may also apply;
3	Some families are unwilling to use respite care that is not home based;
4	There are very few Asian or African-Caribbean people working in the field of respite care; there are also very few Asian home carers.

Positive measures to respond to these issues include:

Table 19
Positive measures

1	Time Out, a respite care project in Nottingham is developing a black carers' support structure; (*Field Study 10*)
2	Hamara is recruiting and training Asian and African-Caribbean volunteers to provide support to families in their own home; (*Field Study 5*)

9.6 Developing services: training

The field work revealed a great range of training needs. On the one hand there is a requirement for training for professional staff who may be unfamiliar with the issues covered by this report and for carers and volunteers in different support groups and agencies. On the other hand users wanted training mostly of a skill based variety to help with employment and educational advancement.

The main types of training required are as shown below:

Table 20
Types of training

1	For health and social care staff on those specific conditions such as Thalassaemia to reduce misdiagnosis and to assist in the provision of culturally competent services;
2	For carers and peer and other counsellors in coping strategies, bereavement and other loss; genetic counselling; accessing other services;
3	For volunteers in running a voluntary agency including the role of a management committee; working with statutory services; recruiting and managing staff;
4	For some users there is a need for confidence building measures like assertiveness training;
5	For others there is a need for training in language and literacy; BSL and the use of audio equipment and robotronic scanners for blind people;
6	Finally there is a regular demand for all those standard courses that everyone else wants to help them get a job such as computer courses and that disabled people should be able to attend those courses in precisely the same educational facilities as everybody else.

9.7 Developing services: services for women

In discussing the arguments for separate services for black people with a disability we have touched on the specific needs and views of black disabled women. The review found that there were a number of such issues that needed addressing as part of service development, as shown below:

Table 21	
Key issues	
1	Some areas have noted a specific problem of the poor take up of services by black women;
2	Disabled black women in other locations can often live very isolated lives and be excluded from social networks;
3	Disabled black women may simultaneously also be carers themselves either for a child with a disability or a parent;
4	Younger black disabled women may wish to meet separately and for activities that are more linked into education and training;
5	Committees for voluntary sector black disability organisations are sometimes male-dominated;
6	Male partners may be reluctant to allow women with a disability out of the home to attend groups or social activities.

Service development for black women with a disability was a common feature of the fieldwork projects we visited including:

Table 22	
Services for black women	
1	Al Khabirat a self help group for disabled Muslim women in Nottingham; (*Field Study 11*)
2	The Huddersfield African-Caribbean Women's Disability Project; (*Field Study 14*)
3	The Asian Deaf Women's Association runs a multicultural deaf women's group and is linking up with other disabled women's groups in other parts of London; (*Field Study 3*)

10

Disability services in Nottingham and Huddersfield

10.1 Introduction

A major part of the review was to identify two conurbations outside of London with significant ethnic minority populations and where there was a high profile of development of services for black and ethnic minority people with a disability.

In Nottingham we found there to be a wide range of different projects, some of which were highly innovative though with a considerable lack of overall co-ordination. An ethnic minority development worker at the Disabilities Living Centre was acting as a central co-ordinating point but there was little sense of an overall purchasing strategy through health and social care.

In Huddersfield the initiatives had largely flowed from the activities of Kirklees Social Service Departments and the local Family Health Service Associations. The purchasing authorities were concerned about the low take up of disability services by black and ethnic minority people in the area and, therefore, employed a development team to tackle this issue. When initial funding ran out an Asian development officer and an African-Caribbean social worker were retained. Many of the services described were developed as a result of their efforts.

The format for these two area studies is the same as for the individual field studies in other parts of the report.

10.2   **Nottingham**

Field Study 8
The Koshish Stroke Group

History

The Koshish Stroke Group was established by Tish Sood on a voluntary basis. She had previously worked as a fashion designer, but became acutely aware of the issues when her father had a major stroke. A formerly energetic and highly articulate man, after the stroke he was unable to work; refused to use a wheelchair; can only express the odd word and suffers extreme stress and depression. Seeking help for her father she became aware that there was little or no therapy or help for Asian stroke users coming out of hospital.

Services

The group is based in the Indian Community Centre and has been meeting weekly for two years. The majority of the group are non-English speaking and as a consequence of the stroke have major problems with mobility, speech, and manipulation of their hands.

Activities provided included basic movement therapy; tasks to encourage manipulation; different forms of exercise and music.

Alternative therapies are seen as essential and include meditation to help the balance of mind, body and soul; electronic massage, Shiatsu and Tai chi and homeopathy. The co-ordinator, although only a volunteer, is attending courses to improve her skills in these areas.

User progress is monitored carefully and includes one member who can now use family names who previously could not speak and another regaining some use of hands and fingers.

Issues

Some of the users had been referred to an Age Concern Centre, but were unable to use it because they do not speak English.

All of the users are men who are severely disabled and represent a considerable burden and stress for their families. They receive little help from statutory services. This service is entirely voluntary, even the transport being provided in helpers' cars.

The potential for extending the service is considerable and yet without some level of funding, this will not be possible.

The Co-worker Project, Nottingham

History

Nottingham Community Health NHS Trust had been concerned for some time about the limited take-up of community health services by people from ethnic minority communities. A wide range of specialist services, such as physiotherapy, occupational therapy and speech and language therapy were seeing few or no Black or Asian clients.

One potential response is to look to the recruitment of Black and Asian staff in all these professions. The pilot project being established as part of the Community Stroke Service instead is employing 'co-workers' to work with ethnic minority families alongside the health professionals.

Services

Two co-workers – an Asian co-worker, Parveen Riaz, who speaks Mirpuri Punjabi and an African Caribbean co-worker, Jenny Golding, who speaks Patois – have been appointed under the management of Service Co-ordinator, Suzanne Pegg.

In advance of the service opening they have been shadowing some of the professionals listed above, so as to be clear about their role. They will then work with and under the supervision of these staff and others, such as mental health nurse practitioners, psychologists and domestic nurses.

They will each carry a caseload of perhaps six families at any one time, both interpreting the needs of the family to the professional and assisting the professional carry out their role and performing basic functions.

Over the 18 months of the pilot, it is expected that 100 families in total may be helped. The project will be formally evaluated by the University of Nottingham.

Issues

The pilot covers one sixth of the area covered by the NHS Trust including the main concentrations of Asian and African Caribbean communities. The two workers may then untap considerable need which is not currently being met.

Field Study 10
The Time Out Respite Care Project

History
The African and African-Caribbean Respite Care Project (Time Out) was originally funded as a pilot project by the King's Fund. Following formal evaluation, funding has been taken on by Nottingham Social Services Department. Carer structures in Nottingham were previously largely white and there were concerns that many black carers were unlikely to be receiving the same support as their white counterparts.

Initially Time Out identified twenty carers and this has expanded so that there are now over eighty carers on their lists.

Services
Time Out is managed by a Co-ordinator, Denise Morris, and provides five carer support workers each of whom is supporting approximately ten families. Support workers, who are on a 24 hour rota in case of emergencies, go into the family home to provide support whilst the carer goes out shopping, etc. There is no residential respite care for African-Caribbean people in Nottingham though occasionally they can arrange this in Birmingham.

They have now established a register of black carers in the city and provide an information and advice service and a carers' luncheon club.

Those cared for are usually severely disabled requiring 24 hour care. The most common group consists of those who have had a stroke followed by people with diabetes which may have caused blindness or led to an amputation.

Issues
Time Out ideally feels that carers and support workers should have a common culture particularly as regards religion. Language for African-Caribbean people is often under-valued or not recognised as an issue.

Equally important is the issue of 'attitude'. In the view of Denise Morris many health care professionals tend to treat African-Caribbean people with a disability as though they were children and not with due respect. A subsidiary issue is the knowledge that their support workers have of matters like skin and health care, diet, etc.

Issues for younger people
At present the service is only available to carers looking for someone aged 55 or over and they would like to expand the service to deal with carers for young people.

Field Study 11
The Ethnic Outreach Project, Disabilities Living Centre

History

The role of the Disabilities Living Centre is to provide advice and information on equipment for people with a disability. The Centre has a wide range of equipment on display which can be demonstrated and tested. The Centre was concerned about the low take up of their services by Asian and African-Caribbean people despite being located in the heart of these communities.

Services

The Ethnic Outreach Project was established to promote the service to ethnic minority groups and to date the Project Development Worker, Shahnaz Aziz, has been making presentations to community groups and preparing leaflets and posters. She is also preparing training packs on ethnicity and disability for local health care professionals. From her initial round of outreach visits it became apparent that there are a number of community-based organisations for Asian and African-Caribbean people who are beginning to be concerned about or providing services for people with a disability. Some of these groups are informal or newly founded and usually lacking resources. There is no effective co-ordination or development support for this activity and, therefore, Shahnaz has had to broaden her role to include a networking role.

Issues

It is already apparent that problems with the take up of the service are not limited to a simple lack of knowledge about its role. Many potential users would be very interested in using the equipment on offer but it is far too expensive for them. There is considerable poverty amongst the local Mirpuri Pakistani community which means that many of the more sophisticated items are well beyond their reach.

Despite its location it is likely that the Centre will need to go further than simply promoting its range of equipment if it wishes to serve the local ethnic minority communities. There is probably a good case for broadening the Ethnic Outreach Project to include development and group work with ethnic minority communities. As well as working closely with the Nottingham projects described above Shahnaz has also been working with the following groups in the area:

Al Khabirat is a self help group for disabled and elderly Asian women run by Nasreen Khan, Organiser for Day Care for the Muslim Women's Organisation. New premises are being developed which will include disabled access. They are aware of significant numbers of Asian women with a disability who are not using services.

Veronica Barnes has recently been employed by The Marcus Garvey Centre which provides a range of day care services for African-Caribbean users. A significant number of users have a disability including those who have had strokes; people with visual and hearing impairment and the Centre now wishes to develop specific services. Immediately a Black Alzheimers' Group is being established.

Surinder Bawa is a Community Development Worker for Rushcliff Social Services who has been involved in group work in the area. Following a house to house survey she has now established a group for Asian people with a disability which consists of six people with mobility problems, one who is visually impaired and one who is deaf.

10.3   **Huddersfield**

Field Study 12

The Community Support Team, Huddersfield Disability Centre, Kirklees Social Services Department

History

Mohammad Munir and Phil James – the current development officers for this service – were originally employed to undertake research into the low level of take up of services by black and ethnic minority people with a disability. (See below for separate section on the work of Phil James.)

This led to five posts being funded through Section 11 funding from the Home Office. As all five staff members came from outside of the area the initial need was for a thorough process of networking with community groups. The net result was that take up of disability services generally within Huddersfield increased from 2 to 15%.

Now that the Section 11 funding has ceased the two development posts have been retained and are funded directly by Social Services.

Services

Mohammad Munir now runs two groups for Asian people with a disability – the Paddock Asian Men's Group and an integrated Batley Women's Group, Marhaba.

The Paddock Group has been meeting for eighteen months and is funded by a small grant from Social Services. It was set up by introducing individual clients to each other who, although they lived close to each other were not in contact. Existing day centres were primarily used by white people and Asian users were reluctant to use them for reasons of language and diet. There are now fifteen members meeting weekly. They are all in their early 20's and wheelchair users. Sessional tutors are provided and courses include cooking, managing on a budget and so on.

The Marhaba group originally met in an Asian Day Centre. However, when the eligibility criteria were tightened younger women found themselves excluded and as a consequence a self help group was established. It now consists of twenty women with mobility problems or visual impairment. Activities include trips, inviting speakers, sessions on welfare benefits, flower arranging and basic computer skills.

Mohammad then undertakes individual case work with Asian people with a disability. He describes this as a 'holistic' assessment looking at social and educational needs as well as the need for aids and adaptations.

Issues

There has been resentment to the development of these services and those for African-Caribbean users from workers who feel that ethnic minority clients are receiving more services than white.

contd

The demand for home care is rising but there are no Asian or Black home care workers. Mohammad feels that many Asian women would like to become home carers but are prevented because they are unable to complete the forms and are unfamiliar with the recruitment process. The main Day Centres in Huddersfield do not have any Asian care staff.

There is a higher incidence of disability including deafness and blindness in Pakistani families and the project estimates that it is 15% higher than the average.

Issues for younger people

Many families are regarded as being too protective of a young person with a disability and may under-estimate the potential for personal development seeing the disability as God's will.

Many younger disabled people are keen to live independently though there is often parental resistance. The project has helped a number move to independent specially adapted flats.

Field Study 13
The Sickle Cell and Thalassaemia Project

History

Phil James, one of the Development Workers at the Disability Centre (see above) had undertaken research into services for people with Sickle Cell and Thalassaemia. The research indicated that the limited services that were available, were unco-ordinated and patchy and that people with the illness were often isolated and without support.

A bid for Joint Finance was made to establish the project and to set up a peer counselling group. Initially they had no idea how many people had the conditions and so outreach work was undertaken including phone-ins on community radio.

Services

After four months of outreach 16 people offered to become involved in the peer counselling project and nine have now trained to become peer counsellors and provide advice and information. Of the nine, four have full blown Sickle Cell and five have the trait.

The training has included race and disability; the medical aspects of the illnesses; basic concepts of counselling; bereavement, grief and loss; and genetic counselling for couples.

Work to date has primarily been with African-Caribbean users and the Project now wishes to appoint a second development worker for Asian people.

contd

Issues

Many professionals are not aware of the symptomology of these illnesses and so teachers may misinterpret children with the condition as lazy, etc.

There is no routine screening for these conditions and accurate diagnosis will only occur where a patient requires a blood test for other purposes.

Field Study 14
The African-Caribbean Women's Disability Project

History

This service was initiated by the Development Worker at the Disability Centre who was concerned about the poor take up of services by black women. Funding was obtained for a Development Worker and the group now has a meeting room and offices in a local Business Centre.

Services

Seventy women are now members of the project and forty five of these attend regularly. Groups may have as many as eighteen women participating.

The project offers support and advocacy to users and undertakes assessments of new users. There are fortnightly meetings with guest speakers on benefits and health issues.

The project is run by a small committee of women some of whom have disabilities. Disabled members also undertake computer and administration tasks. They are now setting up a volunteers group.

Information, advice and support services on health issues, employment and training are provided for African-Caribbean disabled women and carers.

Issues

Some of the women are carers for people with a disability as well as having a disability themselves.

Younger users are very keen to gain paid employment but are not receiving the skills training they require.

The issue of 'pride' was highlighted as a reason for women not accessing welfare benefits.

11

Key Medical Conditions

11.1	Sickle Cell Disease

Sickle cell is a condition which is prevalent in people of African/Caribbean descent. Sickle cell disease is a serious blood disorder affecting the shape of the red blood cells which are sickle shaped, rather than crescent shaped. This affects the ability of these cells to flow through blood vessels which can result in obstruction of the vessels and damage to bones and tissue which are denied oxygen. Sickle cell can affect individuals differently from people experiencing fairly lengthy periods of good health to frequent admissions to hospitals and severe pain.

11.2	Thalassaemia

Thalassaemia is known to affect people from South Asia, Southern Europe and the Middle East. As with Sickle cell disorder, Thalassaemia also affects the structure or synthesis of haemoglobin.

Thalassaemia is a serious blood disorder which can result in severe anaemia from very early childhood. In the most severe cases repeated blood transfusions are required to maintain life. The condition is an inherited blood disorder with 25% of parents who carry the gene having a child with the condition. The only treatment for someone suffering from Thalassaemia is regular blood transfusions every 4 weeks, with further, more complicated treatment being necessary for adults with the condition.

11.3	Lupus

This is an auto-immune disease, rather than a genetic disease, therefore the link with ethnicity is circumstantial. The condition affects predominantly women of child bearing years, although children, men and the elderly can also be affected. There is a greater predominance in women of African-Caribbean descent. The symptoms are varied and can include tiredness, inflammation in the blood leading to swollen joints, fatigue, general malaise, skin rashes and kidney, heart, liver and nervous system complaints. Lupus is known as the great 'imitator', as it is often misdiagnosed. However, there is a growing awareness around this condition amongst GPs and other medical professionals.

12

The consultation exercise with statutory and voluntary providers

12.1 Introduction

One of the preliminary stages of the review was to construct contact lists of lead officers in Health and Social Service Authorities. We then wrote to those lead officers (or Directors / Chief Executives where we were unable to identify a lead officer) with a basic questionnaire requesting information on black and ethnic minority clients' use of disability services. A similar format was sent to major disability organisations in the independent sector.

The intention was not to undertake some rigorous statistical analysis of service usage but instead to obtain information on the key issues and on any responses to those key issues in terms of service development. In particular, we saw this as a route to making contact with some of the smaller localised self-help and other groups. The key questions asked were:

- what specific issues are you aware of with regard to black and ethnic minority people with a disability?

- what specific services are you providing?

- are there any self help or other groups for black and ethnic minority people in your area that are worth contacting?

The substance of the answers we received is included in the Issues sections of this report in previous chapters. However, there some other general observations arising from the responses which are worth commenting on.

12.2 Health authorities

Questionnaires were sent to all the lead officers for disability in 73 Health Authorities. The common response in terms of ethnic monitoring was that there was now a requirement from April 1995 to undertake this for in-patients but not for out-patients or community based services. Nonetheless a small number of Authorities had extended ethnic monitoring more widely but results were, by and large, not available at this stage.

Very little was being done in terms of improving access arrangements for ethnic minority clients to the services available. The only specific facility referred to with any regularity was the provision of interpreters.

| 12.3 | Social services |

Questionnaires were sent out to the 108 Social Services Departments addressed to the lead officers for disability.

A considerable number of the departments were unable to provide any statistical data on the ethnic breakdown of the clients they were seeing. On the whole the numbers of clients being seen by departments that did monitor ethnicity was low, with the exception of a few councils which covered areas with high concentrations of black and ethnic minority populations, namely Newham, Waltham Forest, Kingston-upon-Thames.

The questionnaire requested information on the particular types of disability being experienced, by people from ethnic minority groups. The main disabilities highlighted, in order of prevalence were as follows :

- hearing impairment;
- visual impairment;
- learning disabilities;
- cerebral palsy.

The work being undertaken to improve access arrangements for ethnic minority clients was described as follows:

- specific strategies being developed by Equal Opportunities sub-groups;
- anti-discriminatory policies being developed;
- the translation of publicity material;
- the employment of ethnic specialist workers.

| 12.4 | Voluntary agencies |

A total of 120 voluntary agencies were sent the questionnaire. Of these 40 returned the questionnaire. On the whole voluntary agencies were the most likely to monitor ethnicity of users. However, 16 agencies responded that they did not hold any statistics.

The volume of ethnic minority clients using services was also greater with voluntary agencies, with agencies such as the Asian People's Disability Alliance stating that they were seeing in excess of 200 Asian clients.

The questionnaire asked agencies to identify any specific needs particular to eth-nic minority clients which were not being addressed. The following areas were identified :

1. Take-up of services – this was something that was still not happening with ethnic minority clients.

2. An analysis of the appropriateness of current services.

3. Translators and interpreters as a standard part of the service.

4. A general under-resourcing of specific services, e.g. services to the Somali communities, refugees.

5. A recognition of sickle cell and its implication for the African-Caribbean population in particular.

6. The particular needs of women, children, profoundly deaf individuals and the elderly.

13

Bibliography

1. ADAPT, *Asian and Disabled — A Study into the needs of Asian people with disabilities in the Bradford Area*, Spastics Society and Barnardo's, July 1993.

2. Abida Akram, *Race and Disability Action Planning (Stage 2)*, L.B. Waltham Forest (Disability Equality & Race Relations Committee)

3. L. Appleton, N. Lewis and A. Copestake, *The London Disability Guide — A resource book for disabled people living in London*, GLAD, 1994.

4. K Atkin and J Rollings, *Community Care in a Multi-Racial Britain*, A Critical Review of the Literature, Social Policy Research Unit, 1993.

5. Hasan Badat and Deborah Whall-Roberts, *Bridging the Gap — Creating services for deaf people from ethnic minority communities*, RNID, 1994.

6. Nasa Begum and Sheila Fletcher, *Improving Disability Services — The way forward for health and social services*, Living Options Partnership.

7. Nasa Begum, *Something to be proud of — The lives of Asian disabled people and carers in Waltham Forest*, L.B. Waltham Forest, May 1992.

8. Nasa Begum, *Beyond Samosas & Reggae — A guide to developing services for Black disabled people*, The King's Fund, 1995.

9. Nasa Begum, Mildrette Hill and Andy Stevens, *Reflections — The Views of Black Disabled People on their Lives and Community Care*, GLAD, March 1994.

10. A Bloch, *Information Services: The needs of ethnic minorities*, Policy Studies Institute, 1992.

11. Jeff Chandra, *Facing up to Difference: A toolkit for creating culturally competent services for black and minority ethnic communities*, The King's Fund, 1996.

12. A Darnborough and D Kinrade, *Directory for Disabled People — A handbook of information for everyone involved with disability*, RADAR, 1994.

13. *The Health Panel for Minority Ethnic Communities in and around Dewsbury*, End of year report, 1994.

14. The Steering Group for the Health Panel for Minority Ethnic Communities in and around Dewsbury, *Report*, May 1995.

15. *An agenda for the 1990s*, Disability Manifesto.

16. EDGE (Ethnic Disabled Group Emerging), *Annual Report 1994-5*.

17. Yasmin Gunaratnam, *Checklist on Health and Race — A starting point for managers on improving services for black populations*, The King's Fund, 1993.

18. *Equal Access Action Plan — Progress update: Social services and housing directorate*, L.B. Harrow, Community Liaison Panel, October 1994.

19. Millee Hill, *Race Equality and Service Development*, The King's Fund, 1994.

20. M Hirst and S Baldwin, *Unequal Opportunities — Growing up disabled*, Social Policy Research Unit, 1994.

21. G. Karmi, *The Ethnic Health Handbook*, Blackwell Science, 1996.

22. John Keep and Jill Clarkson, *Disabled People have Rights*, RADAR, October 1994.

23. Caron Kelly and Anjula Kainth, *Ethnic Monitoring of Service Provision – 1993*, L.B. Waltham Forest, Social Services, Social Justice.

24. *Information Line – Continuation and Expansion of Services*, Report by DSS, Lambeth Social Services Committee, February 1995.

25. A MacFarlane and L Laurie, *Demolishing 'Special Needs' – Fundamental principles of non-discriminatory housing*, The British Council of Organisations for Disabled People, 1996.

26. Jean Martin, Howard Meltzer and David Elliot, *The Prevalence of Disability among Adults*, OPCS Surveys of Disability in Great Britain, Report 1, HMSO, 1988.

27. *New Directions*, The Newsletter of Good Practices in Mental Health, Winter 1995.

28. *Race and Disability*, A Dialogue for Action, Conference Report, May 1991.

29. RADAR, Education Factsheet 1, *The Education Act 1981*, March 1991.

30. RADAR, Education Factsheet 2, *Assessment under the Education Act 1981 (Section 5) – Notes for parents and voluntary organisations*, April 1991

31. RADAR, *A Guide to RADAR*.

32. RADAR Bulletin, No. 253, October 1995.

33. RADAR, *A summary of the Disabled Persons (Services, Consultation and Representation) Act 1986*, March 1989.

34. RADAR, *Summary of the findings of OPCS Reports 3 and 5 concerning the prevalence of disability amongst children and the financial circumstances of families with disabled children living in private households*, August 1989.

35. *Reflections – The Views of Black Disabled People on their Lives and Community Care*, CCETSW, Paper 32.3, March 1994.

36. *Campaign News*, No. 10 Summer/Autumn 1995, SCOPE.

37. Arvind Sharma and David Love, *A Change in Approach – A report on the experience of deaf people from black and ethnic minority communities*, DoH

38. Mike Silvera, Dave Miller, Carolyn Clarke, *Core Health and Race Standards*, Good practice paper, The King's Fund, January 1996.

39. Singh, *Black and Physically Disabled: Benefits take-up project*, Ethnic Minorities Service Team, Leicestershire Social Services Department, 1993.

40. C Smaje, *Health, 'Race' and Ethnicity – Making Sense of the Evidence*, The King's Fund Institute, 1995.

41. M Storkey, *London's Ethnic Communities – One city many communities*, London Research Centre, 1994.

42. Stuart, "Race and Disability – Just a Double Oppression?", in *Disability, Handicap and Society*, Volume 7 Number 2, 1992.

43. *Within Reach: Access for disabled children to mainstream education*, The National Union of Teachers in association with The Spastics Society, 17 August 1992.

14

Directory of disability services

1

Organisation:	**African-Caribbean Disablement Association**
Address:	Unit 14, Alpha Business Centre, South Grove, Walthamstow, London E17 7NX
Telephone No:	0181 521 6429
Contact Person:	Jennifer Ennis
Position:	Project Development Manager
Services:	ACDA offers support, information, advice to members of the African-Caribbean community who have a disability. Social and recreational events are also organised ACDA aims to raise awareness of the issues facing African-Caribbean disabled people enabling greater access to services and employment.

2

Organisation:	**African Community Care Project**
Address:	53 Islington Park Street, London N1 1QB
Telephone No:	0171 359 0827
Contact Person:	Mr Opong
Position:	Hon Secretary
Services:	The organisation offers a home visiting service, a drop in centre, and an African meals-on-wheels service. The home visiting service includes cleaning the homes of clients, assisting in looking after disabled and elderly people, offering a respite service to carers and offering support and advice. The drop in centre provides advice and information on health, welfare rights , and legal matters.

3

Organisation:	**Asian Deaf Women's Association**
Address:	53 The Broadway, Stratford, London E15 4BQ
Telephone No:	0181 221 0581 (voice/answering machine)
Minicom:	0181 555 9680 (answering machine)
Fax:	0181 221 0582
Contact Person:	Sarla Meisuria
Position:	Outreach/Information Worker
Services:	ADWA provides counselling for Asian women and girls who are deaf or hard of hearing and who may be experiencing difficulties in coping with everyday life, emotional problems, family issues, etc. ADWA understands the needs of Asian Deaf Women and employs staff who are aware of the issues. The organisation also provides basic BSL communication, and provides information on further education, health awareness issues and organises social activities.

4

Organisation:	**Asian Parents Association for Special Education Needs in Tower Hamlets (APASENTH)**
Address:	The Brady Centre, 192-196 Hanbury Street, London E1
Telephone No:	0171 375 0554
Contact Person:	Shofiur Rahman
Position:	Project Co-ordinator
Services:	APASENTH provides a range of services to over 200 Bangladeshi families who care for children and adults with a range of disabilities. APASENTH provides advice on welfare rights, education, housing and health. The organisation holds a weekly parents support group and employs an S.E.N. Development worker whose role is to help parents with school liaison, school reviews and provide an interpreting service. A Day Care Project provides culturally sensitive day care to Bangladeshi adults with disabilities and a range of social and cultural activities are held. Other activities include a summer Project providing educational day trips for children with disabilities and a life skills project for girls.

5

Organisation:	**Asian People with Disabilities Alliance (APDA)**
Address:	Disability Alliance Centre, The Old Refectory, Central Middlesex Hospital, London NW10 7NS
Telephone No:	0181 961 2797
Contact Person:	Mahesh Amin
Position:	Respite Care Co-ordinator
Services:	APDA aims to promote access to services for Asian people with disabilities and their carers, and is able to match the services it provides to the needs of Asian people. APDA provides services which take into account Asian traditions, practices and family relationships. APDA also runs a Day Respite Centre, specifically equipped for disabled users, the activities provided include; Asian Music and Art Therapy, Independent Living Skills, Relaxation, Peer counselling in Asian languages, Users and Carers forum. APDA also provides information, advice and case management in several Asian languages and enables people to access services such as welfare benefits, housing, holidays, education employment and training, etc.

6

Organisation:	**Barnado's Hamara Family Project**
Address:	1B Priory Avenue, Walthamstow, London E17 7QP
Telephone No:	0181 503 7270
Contact Person:	Andrea De Berker
Position:	Project Leader
Services:	The Project provides family based respite care services for children with disability living in Waltham Forest. Services include a Sitting Service and a Volunteer Service. The family based care links the family and child to a local carer, who has received training from the Project. The purpose of the service is to enable the child to be left with a carer when the parents need a break. The sitting service links the family and the child to a sitter who has been prepared and assessed by the Project. The sitter looks after the child in their own

home for periods of up to 4 hours a time. The volunteer service is designed to give the disabled child an opportunity to enjoy a more full and varied social life. The child is linked to a volunteer who can take the child out to enjoy activities of the child's choice.

7

Organisation:	**Black and Asian Disability Group**
Address:	The College of Continuing Education in Walsall, Whitehall School, Weston Street, Walsall WS1 4BQ
Telephone No:	01922 724 869
Contact Person:	Arvin Parmar
Position:	Secretary
Services:	BADG offers support, advice, information, representation and advocacy to Black and Asian people with disabilities. BADG also hold quarterly carers meetings, provides a meals on wheels service, a helpline and befriending service.

8

Organisation:	**Community Care Service for the African-Caribbean Community**
Address:	Afro-Caribbean Educational Project, Women's Centre, 603 High Road, Leyton, London E10 6RF
Telephone No:	0181 923 9323
Contact Person:	Nina Sikod
Position:	Domiciliary Home Care Co-ordinator
Services:	The organisation aims to provide personal and domestic care, advice and support, to frail, disabled and elderly African-Caribbean individuals who need help to live in their own homes in the community, preventing admission into residential care or hospital. Home care services include: personal care, washing and bathing, dressing, assistance with toilet needs, administration with toilet needs, administration of medicines – under guidance. Domestic care which includes: general cleaning, pension collection, laundry, shopping, preparing and cooking food. An assessment is carried out and a nominal fee of £5.00 is charged for home care services.

9

Organisation:	**Disabilities Living Centre**
Address:	Lenton Business Centre, Lenton Boulevard, Nottingham NG7 2BY
Telephone No:	0115 942 0391
Contact Person:	Shahnaz Aziz
Position:	Project Development Worker
Services:	The centre provides information and advice on equipment and services for people with disabilities, elderly people, their carers and professional staff. A worker has been appointed to promote this service to ethnic minority groups and to set up training on ethnicity and disability for professionals working in the field.

10

Organisation:	**Disability Services**
Address:	Zetland Street, Huddersfield HD1 2RA
Telephone No:	01484 453000
Contact Person:	Mohammed Munir
Position:	Development Officer
Services:	The community support team is based at Disability Services, their brief is to work with disabled people throughout Kirklees. The aim being to improve service take up by Black and ethnic minority groups and to improve service delivery to these clients through involvement and participation in the development of services and access to information.

11

Organisation:	**EKTA Luncheon Club**
Address:	Rushcliff Social Services, The Hall, Bridgford Road, West Bridgford, Nottingham NG2 6AD
Telephone No:	0115 981 8118 ext 267
Contact Person:	Surinder Bawa
Position:	Community Care Officer
Services:	A luncheon club was set up as a result of a house to house survey measuring the needs and requirements of the Asian community in Rushcliff. There are currently 30 users of the luncheon club service, a number of whom have disabilities: the activities include table games and Summer outings. The club is open to Asian people over the age of 50, and caters for those requiring special diets and transport is available for users of the service. The club is now looking for premises which are suitable for disabled people, and which will enable the club to develop the services currently being offered.

12

Organisation:	**Huddersfield African-Caribbean Women's Disability Project**
Address:	Ray Street Enterprise Centre, Unit 4, Ray Street, Huddersfield, West Yorkshire HD1 6BL
Telephone No:	01484 455252
Contact Person:	Cheryl Edwin
Position:	Development Worker
Services:	HACWDP provides advice and information to disabled women and their carers on disability services, welfare benefits, health issues, and employment and training opportunities. HACWDP also provides individual support and holds regular group meetings where women can come together, share ideas and experiences and get away from the social isolation they may feel. There is also the opportunity to listen to presentations on relevant topics requested by the users.

13

Organisation:	**The Indian Community Centre**
Address:	Mosley/Rawson Street, New Basford, Nottingham NG7 7FR
Telephone No:	0115 924 4579 or 978 5985
Contact Person:	Amardeep Singh/Raj Jogia
Position:	Centre Manager
Services:	A Day Centre is provided which is used mainly by Asian elderly and physically disabled people. The Centre offers video and music facilities, light exercise classes, welfare benefits advice, and a group for people who have suffered a stroke (*Koshish*). Speakers are invited to give talks on various subjects and refreshments are available. Freshly prepared Indian meals are provided at subsidised rates for the elderly and physically disabled users. Outings are arranged from time to time. General advice on immigration is available, with solicitors attending the centre to provide information.

14

Organisation:	**Marcus Garvey Day Care Centre**
Address:	Lenton Boulevard, Nottingham NG7 2BY
Telephone No:	0115 979 2906
Contact Person:	Veronica Barnes
Position:	Care Service Manager
Services:	The Marcus Garvey Centre is a Day Centre for African-Caribbean people. The centre runs a luncheon club service and a Black Alzheimers' group is being developed. The centre has approximately 100 members, most of whom are over the age of 45 years. Some users are disabled i.e. visually impaired, with hearing problems or have suffered strokes. A welfare rights advisor attends the centre twice a week and a social worker attends twice a month, providing advice on accessing services.

15

Organisation:	**Nottingham Community Health NHS Trust**
Address:	Mary Potter Hostel, 76 Gregory Boulevard, Nottingham NG7 5HY
Telephone No:	0115 978 4561
Contact Person:	Susanne Peggs
Position:	Pilot Stroke Service Co-ordinator
Services:	This is a 2 year pilot project that aims to provide a needs led service for people who have had a stroke and their carers. Part of the original tender was to investigate models of service provision to meet the needs of the ethnic minorities. The service uses a 'Bilingual Co-Worker' system whereby the Co-worker (who is from an ethnic minority group) is trained to work alongside and under the supervision of professional staff, translating information and explaining what is happening to the patient and providing advice and support to the professional to shape packages of care. The aim therefore is to enable people from the ethnic minority groups to access services that are appropriate to their needs that take into account the linguistic, religious and cultural issues faced by a patient.

16

Organisation:	**Organisation of Blind African-Caribbeans (OBAC)**
Address:	Gloucester House, 8 Camberwell New Road, London SE5 ORX
Telephone No:	0171 735 3400
Contact Person:	Marcia Green
Position:	Information Services Co-Ordinator
Services:	OBAC provides support, advice, information and assistance to partially sighted and blind African and Caribbean people. The welfare and information service includes an advocacy worker who specialises in working with young people, and an outreach worker who mainly works with the elderly. There is also a welfare rights worker who provides advice and information on Guide dogs and aids and adaptations. OBAC also has a Resource Centre, and produces a weekly talking Newsletter; OBAC also produces a talking Newspaper.

17

Organisation:	**Sickle Cell and Thalassaemia Project**
Address:	Disability Services, Zetland Street, Huddersfield HD1 2RA
Telephone No:	01484 452464
Contact Person:	Louise Fleary
Position:	Development worker
Services:	The project provides a peer counselling service for people affected by Sickle Cell or Thalassaemia. People with the condition are trained in counselling skills so that they can support others affected by the condition. A peer counsellor will not give medical advice, but provide support intended to help people take control of their own lives and complement the professional services provided by doctors and nurses.

18

Organisation:	**Waltham Forest Disability Resource Centre**
Address:	1A Warner Road, Walthamstow E17 7DY
Telephone No:	0181 520 8347
Contact Person:	Mrs Mehboob Khan
Position:	Activities Manager
Services:	The DRC offers a varied programme of activities including training, advice sessions, alternative therapies, etc. Specialised equipment is also available including adapted computers, induction loops, Braille equipment and sign language; interpretation is available on request. There are also specialist groups for people who speak community languages, and men only and women only groups. Bilingual staff are available to interpret. A free door to door bus service is available for users of the centre.